Pancreatic Cancer Diet Cookbook for Beginners

Nutritional, Nourishing and Balanced Anti-Cancer Recipes to heal Naturally

Isaac Hendricks

Table of Contents

INTRODUCTION

Understanding Pancreatic Cancer and Nutrition

Pancreatic cancer is a highly aggressive and deadly form of cancer that affects the pancreas, an organ located behind the stomach. It is one of the least understood and most difficult to treat types of cancer, with a five-year survival rate of less than 10%. While there is no cure for pancreatic cancer, proper nutrition can play a crucial role in managing the symptoms and improving the overall quality of life for patients.

The pancreas has two main functions: producing digestive enzymes and producing insulin and glucagon, which regulate blood sugar levels. In pancreatic cancer, tumours can grow in the head, body, or tail of the pancreas, which can lead to a variety of symptoms depending on the location. Some common symptoms include abdominal pain, weight loss, jaundice, and diabetes.

One of the most challenging aspects of managing pancreatic cancer is dealing with the side effects of treatment, such as nausea, vomiting, and fatigue. A healthy diet can help alleviate these symptoms by providing the body with the nutrients it needs to cope with treatment and maintain a healthy weight.

Here are some nutrition tips for managing pancreatic cancer:

1. Eat small, frequent meals: Instead of three large meals a day, aim for six smaller meals spread throughout the day. This can help prevent nausea and vomiting by keeping your stomach full and reducing the risk of overeating.

2. Focus on high-protein foods: Protein is essential for building and repairing tissues in the body. Good sources of protein include lean meats, poultry, fish, beans, lentils, and tofu.

3. Choose complex carbohydrates: Complex carbohydrates provide sustained energy and are less likely to cause blood sugar spikes than simple carbohydrates. Examples include whole-grain breads, pasta, rice, fruits, and vegetables.

4. Limit fat intake: High-fat foods can be difficult to digest and may cause discomfort or diarrhoea in some patients. Aim for healthy fats such as those found in nuts, seeds, avocados, and olive oil.

5. Stay hydrated: Dehydration is common in patients with pancreatic cancer due to nausea or blockages in the digestive system. Drink plenty of water all day to stay hydrated.

6. Consult a registered dietitian: A registered dietitian can provide personalised nutrition guidance based on your specific needs and treatment plan. They can also help you manage any dietary restrictions or intolerances that may arise during treatment.

In conclusion, understanding pancreatic cancer and nutrition is essential for managing this challenging disease. By following these tips and working closely with your healthcare team and a registered dietitian, you can improve your overall health and well-being during treatment and beyond. Remember to always consult your healthcare provider before making any significant changes to your diet or lifestyle habits.

The Importance of a Healthy Diet During Treatment

Pancreatic cancer is a devastating disease that affects thousands of people worldwide every year. While medical treatments such as surgery, chemotherapy, and radiation therapy can help manage the disease, a healthy diet is equally important during treatment. In this introduction, we will explore the importance of a healthy diet during treatment for pancreatic cancer patients.

Maintaining Nutrition:

Pancreatic cancer can cause several symptoms such as nausea, vomiting, and loss of appetite, making it challenging for patients to maintain a healthy weight. A healthy diet during treatment can help maintain nutrition levels by providing essential nutrients such as protein, carbohydrates, and fats. Protein is necessary for tissue development and repair, whereas carbohydrates offer energy. Fats are necessary for absorbing vitamins and minerals.

Managing Side Effects:

Chemotherapy and radiation therapy can cause several side effects such as mouth sores, diarrhoea, and fatigue. A healthy diet can help manage these side effects by providing foods that are easy to digest and do not irritate the digestive system. For example, foods rich in fibre such as whole grains and fruits should be avoided as they can worsen diarrhoea. Instead, patients should opt for low-fibre foods such as white bread, rice, and pasta.

Boosting Immunity:

Chemotherapy and radiation therapy can weaken the immune system, making patients more susceptible to infections. A healthy diet rich in vitamins and minerals can help boost immunity levels by providing essential nutrients that support the immune system. For example, vitamin C is essential for the production of white blood cells that fight infections. Vitamin C-rich foods include citrus fruits, strawberries, and broccoli.

Reducing Risk of Complications:

Pancreatic cancer patients are at a higher risk of developing complications such as diabetes and malnutrition during treatment. A healthy diet can help reduce the risk of these complications by maintaining a healthy weight and providing essential nutrients. For example, patients should avoid sugary drinks and foods as they can worsen blood sugar levels. Instead, they should opt for complex carbohydrates such as whole grains and fruits that provide sustained energy levels.

In conclusion, a healthy diet is crucial during treatment for pancreatic cancer patients. It helps maintain nutrition levels, manage side effects, boost immunity levels, and reduce the risk of complications. Patients should work with a registered dietitian to develop a personalised meal plan that meets their specific needs during treatment. By following a healthy diet, patients can improve their overall health and well-being during this challenging time.

How to Use This Cookbook

Welcome to the Pancreatic Cancer Diet Cookbook for Beginners! This cookbook is designed to provide you with healthy and delicious meal ideas during your pancreatic cancer treatment. Whether you're a beginner in the kitchen or an experienced cook, this cookbook is for you. Here's how to use it:

1. Consult with Your Healthcare Team:

Before starting any new diet, it's essential to consult with your healthcare team, including your oncologist, nutritionist, and dietitian. They can provide you with personalised dietary recommendations based on your specific needs during treatment.

2. Understand the Recipes:

Each recipe in this cookbook includes a list of ingredients, step-by-step instructions, and nutritional information. Please read through the recipe carefully before starting to ensure you have all the necessary ingredients and understand the cooking process.

3. Modify Recipes to Meet Your Needs:

While we've done our best to provide recipes that are suitable for pancreatic cancer patients, some modifications may be necessary based on your specific needs. For example, if you have difficulty swallowing or digesting certain foods, you may need to puree or blend them before consuming. If you have dietary restrictions or allergies, please adjust the recipe accordingly.

4. Prepare Foods Safely:

To minimise the risk of infection during treatment, it's essential to prepare foods safely. Here are some tips:

- Wash your hands thoroughly before handling food.

- Use separate cutting boards and utensils for raw meat, poultry, and seafood.

- Cook foods thoroughly to kill any bacteria that may cause infection. Use a meat thermometer to ensure that meats reach a safe internal temperature (165°F for poultry and meat).

- Store leftovers in the refrigerator promptly and consume within 3-4 days. Reheat leftovers thoroughly before consuming.

- Avoid unpasteurized dairy products and raw or undercooked eggs.

- Wash fruits and vegetables thoroughly before consuming. Consider peeling or washing produce with a vegetable wash or vinegar solution to remove any bacteria that may be present on the skin.

5. Enjoy Your Meals:

Most importantly, enjoy your meals! Eating healthy and delicious foods can help improve your overall health and well-being during treatment. Remember to listen to your body and eat foods that make you feel happy. If you have any questions or concerns about your diet during treatment, please consult with your healthcare team.

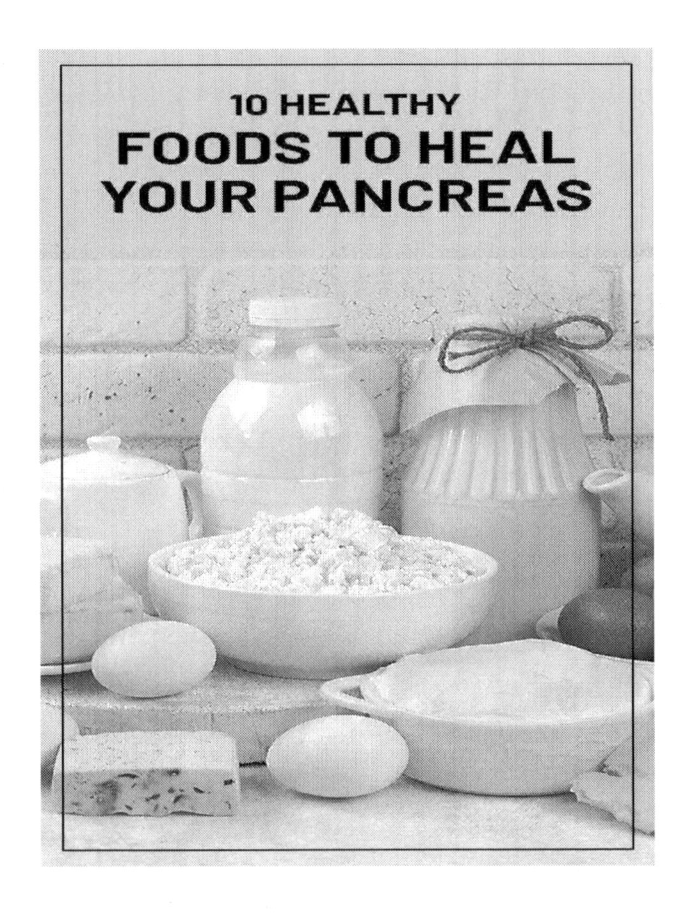

CHAPTER ONE

Pancreatic Cancer Diet Basics

Key Nutritional Considerations

Pancreatic cancer is a devastating disease that affects the pancreas, an organ that plays a crucial role in digestion and metabolism. The disease can cause various symptoms, such as weight loss, fatigue, and abdominal pain, which can lead to malnutrition. Proper nutrition is essential for managing symptoms, maintaining strength, and improving overall health during pancreatic cancer treatment. Here are some key nutritional considerations for the pancreatic cancer diet basics:

- Protein: Pancreatic cancer can cause a decrease in protein production by the pancreas, leading to protein malnutrition. It's crucial to consume enough protein to maintain muscle mass and promote wound healing. Lean sources of protein such as chicken, fish, eggs, and legumes are recommended.

- Carbohydrates: Pancreatic cancer can also affect the body's ability to digest carbohydrates due to a decrease in enzyme production by the pancreas. It's essential to consume complex carbohydrates such as whole grains, fruits, and vegetables that are rich in fibre to promote bowel regularity and prevent constipation.

- Fat: Fats are an essential source of energy and help absorb vitamins A, D, E, and K. However, high-fat foods can cause discomfort due to delayed emptying of the stomach. It's recommended to consume healthy fats such as olive oil, avocado, nuts, and seeds in moderation.

- Hydration: Dehydration is common in individuals with pancreatic cancer due to decreased fluid intake or increased fluid loss from vomiting or diarrhoea. It's crucial to drink plenty of fluids throughout the day to prevent dehydration and maintain electrolyte balance.

- Vitamin and Mineral Supplements: Pancreatic cancer can lead to malabsorption of vitamins and minerals due to decreased enzyme production by the pancreas. It's recommended to consult with a healthcare provider regarding vitamin and mineral supplements to prevent deficiencies.

- Alcohol: Alcohol should be avoided or consumed in moderation as it can irritate the stomach lining and worsen symptoms such as nausea and vomiting.

- Consult with a Registered Dietitian: A registered dietitian can provide personalised nutrition recommendations based on individual needs and preferences during pancreatic cancer treatment. They can also help manage symptoms such as loss of appetite, taste changes, and food intolerances.

Recommended Foods and Ingredients

Pancreatic cancer is a devastating disease that affects the pancreas, an organ located behind the stomach. Unfortunately, pancreatic cancer is often diagnosed at a late stage, making it challenging to treat effectively. While there is no specific diet that can cure pancreatic cancer, certain foods and ingredients may help manage symptoms and support overall health during treatment. Here are some recommended foods and ingredients for the pancreatic cancer diet basics:

1. Protein: Protein is essential for building and repairing cells in the body. People with pancreatic cancer may have difficulty digesting protein due to the disease's impact on the pancreas. To make protein more digestible, it's best to consume small portions of lean protein sources like chicken, fish, and tofu throughout the day instead of large meals.

2. Fibre: Fibre helps promote healthy digestion, which is crucial for people with pancreatic cancer as they may experience constipation due to the disease's impact on the digestive system. Foods rich in fibre include whole grains, fruits, and vegetables.

3. Healthy Fats: Healthy fats like those found in avocados, nuts, and olive oil can help support overall health during treatment. These fats can also help absorb fat-soluble vitamins like vitamin A, D, E, and K.

4. Hydration: Staying hydrated is essential for people with pancreatic cancer as dehydration can worsen symptoms like fatigue and nausea. Drinking enough of water throughout the day can assist to avoid dehydration.

5. Vitamins and Minerals: People with pancreatic cancer may have difficulty absorbing certain vitamins and minerals due to the disease's impact on the pancreas's function. To ensure adequate intake of these nutrients, it may be helpful to take supplements under the guidance of a healthcare provider.

6. Limit Sugar: High sugar intake can lead to weight gain, which can put additional strain on the body during treatment. It's best to limit sugary foods and drinks like candy, soda, and fruit juice.

7. Consult a Dietitian: A registered dietitian can provide personalised nutrition guidance based on individual needs and preferences during pancreatic cancer treatment. They can also offer strategies to manage symptoms like loss of appetite or taste changes that may arise during treatment.

In conclusion, while there is no specific diet that can cure pancreatic cancer, making healthy food choices can help manage symptoms and support overall health during treatment. It's essential to consult a healthcare provider or registered dietitian for personalised nutrition guidance during this challenging time.

Meal Planning and Preparation

Tips for Meal Planning and Preparation

Meal planning and preparation are crucial for individuals with pancreatic cancer as they may experience symptoms such as nausea, vomiting, and fatigue, making it challenging to eat a balanced diet.
Here are some tips for meal planning and preparation in the pancreatic cancer diet cookbook for beginners:

1. Consult with a registered dietitian: A dietitian can help you create a personalized meal plan based on your specific needs and preferences. They can also provide guidance on how to manage symptoms such as diarrhea, constipation, and weight loss.

2. Focus on small, frequent meals: Eating small, frequent meals throughout the day can help manage symptoms such as nausea and fatigue. This approach also allows for better nutrient absorption and reduces the risk of indigestion.

3. Incorporate protein-rich foods: Protein is essential for building and repairing tissues, and individuals with pancreatic cancer may require more protein than usual due to malnutrition. Good sources of protein include lean meats, poultry, fish, beans, and lentils.

4. Choose low-fat options: High-fat foods can be difficult to digest and may cause discomfort. Opt for low-fat options such as skinless chicken, lean cuts of beef, and low-fat dairy products.

5. Limit fiber intake: High-fiber foods can cause bloating and discomfort in individuals with pancreatic cancer. Choose low-fiber options such as white bread, pasta, and rice instead of whole-grain options.

6. Incorporate healthy fats: Healthy fats such as olive oil, avocado, and nuts can help provide energy and essential nutrients. Just be sure to consume them in moderation due to their high calorie content.

7. Stay hydrated: Dehydration is common in individuals with pancreatic cancer due to decreased fluid intake and increased urine output. Aim to drink at least eight glasses of water per day and limit caffeinated beverages that can contribute to dehydration.

8. Plan ahead: Prepare meals in advance to ensure you have healthy options readily available when you're feeling too tired or unwell to cook. This can also help reduce food waste and save time during busy weeks.

9. Experiment with new recipes: Trying new recipes can help keep meals interesting and provide variety in your diet. Look for recipes that are easy to prepare and incorporate the tips mentioned above for a healthy and balanced meal plan.

Sample Meal Plans for Different Stages of Treatment

Pancreatic cancer is a devastating disease that affects not only the patient's health but also their dietary needs. As the disease progresses, the patient's ability to eat and digest food may change, requiring different meal plans at different stages of treatment. In this article, we will provide sample meal plans for three stages of treatment: pre-treatment, during treatment, and post-treatment.

Pre-Treatment Meal Plan

Before starting treatment, the patient's goal is to maintain a healthy weight and build up their strength. The following meal plan can help the patient achieve this:

Breakfast:

- 1 cup of oatmeal with 1/2 cup of blueberries and 1/2 cup of almond milk
- 1 hard-boiled egg
- 1 slice of whole grain toast with 1 tablespoon of peanut butter

Morning Snack:

- Combine 1 small apple with 1 tablespoon almond butter.

Lunch:

- 2 cups of mixed greens with 1/2 cup of cherry tomatoes, 1/4 cup of sliced cucumber, and 1/4 cup of sliced carrots
- 3 oz. Grilled chicken breast
- 1 small whole grain roll with 1 tablespoon of olive oil and balsamic vinegar dressing

Afternoon Snack:

- 1 small banana with 1 tablespoon of honey

Dinner:
- 3 oz. Baked salmon with lemon and dill seasoning
- 1 cup of quinoa with 1/2 cup of steamed broccoli and 1/2 cup of steamed green beans
- 1 small whole grain roll with 1 tablespoon of olive oil and balsamic vinegar dressing

During Treatment Meal Plan

During treatment, the patient may experience side effects such as nausea, vomiting, and fatigue. The following meal plan can help the patient manage these symptoms:

Breakfast:
- 1 small banana blended with 1/2 cup of almond milk and 1 tablespoon of honey (smoothie)
- 1 hard-boiled egg
- 1 small whole grain roll with 1 tablespoon of olive oil and balsamic vinegar dressing (optional)

Morning Snack:
- 1 small apple sliced with cinnamon (optional)

Lunch:
- 2 cups of chicken or vegetable broth (low sodium) with cooked rice or pasta (optional)
- Saltine crackers or ginger snaps (optional) for nausea relief (optional)

Afternoon Snack:

- A few sips of ginger tea (optional) for nausea relief (optional)

Dinner:

- A small portion (about the size of a deck of cards) of cooked vegetables or fruits blended into a puree or soup (optional) for easy digestion (optional)
- Saltine crackers or ginger snaps (optional) for nausea relief (optional) before bedtime (optional) if needed.

Post-Treatment Meal Plan

After completing treatment, the patient's goal is to rebuild their strength and maintain a healthy weight. The following meal plan can help the patient achieve this:

Breakfast:

- 1 cup of oatmeal with blueberries and almond milk (optional) or a scrambled egg with whole grain toast and avocado (optional) for healthy fats. Morning Snack:
- A small apple or banana with almond butter (optional) or a handful of grapes or berries. Lunch:
- Grilled chicken breast or turkey burger on a whole grain bun with lettuce, tomato, avocado, and mustard dressing (optional).

Afternoon Snack:
- A handful of nuts or seeds such as almonds, pumpkin seeds, or sunflower seeds for healthy fats and protein.

Dinner:
- Baked salmon or grilled steak with roasted vegetables such as broccoli, carrots, and sweet potatoes (optional). Remember to always consult your healthcare team for specific dietary recommendations based on your individual needs during each stage of treatment. These meal plans are meant to serve as a guide to help you make healthy choices during your cancer journey.

Grocery Lists and Pantry Staples

Grocery Lists and Pantry Staples in a Pancreatic Cancer Diet Cookbook for Beginners

When dealing with pancreatic cancer, diet plays a crucial role in managing symptoms and supporting overall health. A pancreatic cancer diet cookbook for beginners should include grocery lists and pantry staples to make meal planning and preparation easier. Here are some suggestions:

Grocery List:

Produce:

- Apples (Granny Smith or Honeycrisp)
- Bananas

- Berries (strawberries, raspberries, blueberries)
- Citrus fruits (oranges, lemons, limes)
- Grapes
- Grapefruit
- Kiwi
- Melons (honeydew, cantaloupe)
- Mushrooms (cremini or button)
- Onions (red or yellow)
- Peaches
- Pears
- Pineapple
- Plums
- Spinach or kale
- Tomatoes (cherry or grape)
- Zucchini or summer squash

Protein:

- Boneless, skinless chicken breasts or thighs
- Eggs (whole or egg whites)
- Fish (salmon, cod, tilapia)
- Ground turkey or chicken breast
- Lean beef (flank steak or sirloin)
- Low-fat dairy products (milk, yogurt, cheese)
- Tofu or tempeh (for vegetarian options)

Grains:

- Brown rice (short or long grain).
- Quinoa (rinsed and drained)
- Whole wheat bread or pasta (look for low sugar and low sodium options)
- Oats (rolled or steel cut)
- Popcorn (air popped with no added salt or butter)

Pantry Staples:

(These items can be used to add flavor and nutrition to meals without adding too many calories.)

- Balsamic vinegar
- Canned beans (low sodium varieties such as black beans, kidney beans, chickpeas, and white beans)
- Canned low sodium chicken broth
- Canned low sodium vegetable broth
- Canned low sodium diced tomatoes
- Dijon mustard
- Extra virgin olive oil
- Garlic cloves
- Ginger root
- Herbs and spices (such as basil, oregano, thyme, rosemary, cumin, coriander, turmeric, and red pepper flakes)
- Low sodium soy sauce
- Low sodium tomato sauce
- Low sugar fruit preserves or spreads (such as apricot or peach preserves)
- Low sugar fruit juice (such as apple juice or cranberry juice)
- Low sugar fruit puree (such as unsweetened applesauce)
- Low sugar fruit spreads (such as apricot spread with no added sugar)
- Low sugar ketchup
- Low sugar maple syrup substitute (such as maple flavored syrup with no added sugar)

- Low sugar mustard (such as whole grain mustard with no added sugar)
- Low sugar salad dressings (such as balsamic vinaigrette with no added sugar)
- Low sugar sauces (such as teriyaki sauce with no added sugar)
- Low sugar snacks (such as rice cakes with peanut butter and banana slices on top)

(Note: Always check the nutrition labels for added sugars and sodium.) Based on the passage above, How can I incorporate more protein into my meals while following a pancreatic cancer diet?

CHAPTER TWO

Breakfasts

Overnight Oats with Berries and Almonds

Overnight oats are a healthy and convenient breakfast option for individuals following a pancreatic cancer diet. This recipe for overnight oats with berries and almonds is not only delicious but also packed with nutrients that can help support the body during cancer treatment.

Ingredients:
- 1/2 cup rolled oats
- 1 cup unsweetened almond milk
- 1/2 cup fresh or frozen berries (such as blueberries, raspberries, or strawberries)
- 2 tablespoons chopped almonds
- 1 tablespoon chia seeds (optional)
- 1 tablespoon honey or maple syrup (optional)

Instructions:
1. In a medium-sized mixing bowl, combine rolled oats, almond milk, berries, chopped almonds, and chia seeds (if using). Stir well to combine all ingredients.
2. If desired, add honey or maple syrup to sweeten the mixture to taste. Stir again to combine.

3. Cover the mixing bowl with a lid or plastic wrap and refrigerate overnight (at least 8 hours).
4. In the morning, give the mixture a good stir to ensure that all ingredients are well combined. If the mixture is too thick, add additional almond milk until you get the appropriate consistency.
5. Serve immediately and enjoy your delicious and nutritious breakfast!

Benefits:

This recipe is rich in fiber, protein, and healthy fats, making it a great choice for individuals following a pancreatic cancer diet. Rolled oats are an excellent source of fibre, which can help promote regularity and prevent constipation - a common side effect of cancer treatments. Almond milk is low in calories and fat but high in protein, making it an excellent alternative to dairy milk for individuals who are lactose intolerant or prefer plant-based options. Berries are packed with antioxidants and vitamins C and K, while almonds provide healthy fats and protein that can help keep you feeling full and satisfied throughout the morning.
Chia seeds are rich in omega-3 fatty acids, fibre, and protein, making them an excellent addition to this recipe if desired. Honey or maple syrup can be added for sweetness if desired, but be sure to use them in moderation to avoid adding too many calories or sugar to the recipe.

Spinach and Feta Frittata

Spinach and Feta Frittata: A Nutritious and Delicious Breakfast Option for Pancreatic Cancer Patients

As a pancreatic cancer patient, it's essential to maintain a healthy and balanced diet that supports your body's nutritional needs. While traditional breakfast options like pancakes and waffles may be tempting, they can be high in sugar, fat, and calories, which may not be the best choice for someone undergoing cancer treatment. Instead, consider trying a spinach and feta frittata, a nutritious and delicious breakfast option that's packed with essential nutrients and easy to prepare.

Spinach is an excellent source of iron, vitamin K, and vitamin A, which are essential for maintaining healthy bones, blood cells, and eyesight. Feta cheese is a good source of protein and calcium, which are important for building and maintaining muscle mass and bone health. Eggs are rich in protein and contain essential vitamins and minerals like vitamin D, choline, and phosphorus.

To make a spinach and feta frittata, you'll need:

- 6 large eggs
- 1 cup fresh spinach leaves
- 1/2 cup crumbled feta cheese

- 1/4 cup diced onion
- 1 tablespoon olive oil
- Salt and pepper to taste

Here's how to make it:

1. Preheat your oven to 375°F (190°C).
2. Heat the olive oil in a non-stick skillet over medium heat. Sauté the onion until softened, about 3-4 minutes.
3. Cook the spinach in the skillet until wilted, about 2-3 minutes. Season with salt and pepper to taste.
4. Beat the eggs in a bowl until well combined. Pour the eggs into the skillet with the spinach and onion mixture. Use a spatula to gently stir the mixture until the eggs are set but still moist.
5. Sprinkle the feta cheese over the top of the frittata. Transfer the skillet to the preheated oven and bake for 8-10 minutes or until the cheese is melted and golden brown.
6. Remove from the oven and let it cool for a few minutes before slicing into wedges. Serve hot with a side salad or fresh fruit for added nutrition.

This spinach and feta frittata is not only delicious but also packed with essential nutrients that can help support your body during cancer treatment. It's also easy to prepare, making it a great option for busy mornings when you don't have much time to cook. Give it a try today!

Banana and Almond Butter Smoothie Bowl

This delicious and nutritious breakfast option is perfect for those following a pancreatic cancer diet. It's packed with essential nutrients that can help support overall health and wellbeing, while also being easy to digest.

Ingredients:

- 1 ripe banana
- 1 cup unsweetened almond milk
- 2 tbsp almond butter
- 1 tsp honey (optional)
- 1/2 cup frozen mixed berries
- 1/4 cup rolled oats
- 1 tbsp chia seeds
- 1 tbsp flaxseeds
- 1 tbsp unsweetened shredded coconut

Instructions:

1. In a blender, combine the banana, almond milk, almond butter, and honey (if using). Blend until smooth.
2. Pour the mixture into a bowl and add the frozen mixed berries. Stir gently to combine.
3. Sprinkle the rolled oats, chia seeds, and flaxseeds over the top of the smoothie bowl.
4. Finish with a sprinkle of unsweetened shredded coconut.
5. Serve immediately and enjoy!

This smoothie bowl is rich in fiber, healthy fats, and protein, making it a filling and satisfying breakfast option. The almond butter provides a good source of healthy monounsaturated fats, while the chia and flaxseeds add omega-3 fatty acids and fiber. The frozen mixed berries add a sweet burst of flavor and antioxidants, while the rolled oats provide complex carbohydrates for sustained energy. This smoothie bowl is also low in sugar, making it a great choice for those watching their blood sugar levels. Enjoy this delicious and nutritious breakfast as part of your pancreatic cancer diet!

CHAPTER THREE

Soups and Salads

Chicken Noodle Soup with Vegetables

Ingredients:

- 1 lb boneless, skinless chicken breast, cut into small pieces
- 6 cups low-sodium chicken broth
- 2 medium carrots, peeled and sliced
- 2 celery stalks, sliced
- 1 medium onion, chopped
- 3 garlic cloves, minced
- 2 tbsp olive oil
- 8 oz whole wheat egg noodles
- Salt and pepper to taste
- Fresh parsley or chives for garnish (optional)

Instructions:

1. Heat the olive oil in a big pot over medium heat. Add onion and garlic and sauté until softened, about 3-4 minutes.
2. Add chicken to the pot and cook until browned on all sides, about 5-7 minutes.
3. Add chicken broth, carrots, and celery to the pot. Bring to a boil, then reduce to a low heat and cook until vegetables are soft, about 15-20 minutes.

4. Add egg noodles to the pot and cook according to package instructions. Season with salt and pepper to taste.
5. Serve hot, garnished with fresh parsley or chives if desired. Enjoy your nutritious and delicious Chicken Noodle Soup with Vegetables!

This recipe is a healthy and comforting option for those following a pancreatic cancer diet as it is low in fat and sugar while still providing essential nutrients such as protein from the chicken and fibre from the vegetables and whole wheat noodles. It is also easy to prepare and can be stored in the refrigerator or freezer for later consumption.

Broccoli Cauliflower Soup with Ginger and Turmeric

Broccoli and cauliflower are both cruciferous vegetables that are rich in nutrients and antioxidants. They are also low in calories and carbohydrates, making them an excellent choice for individuals following a pancreatic cancer diet. In this recipe, we will be making a delicious and healthy broccoli cauliflower soup with the added benefits of ginger and turmeric, both of which have anti-inflammatory properties that can help support overall health.

Ingredients:
- 1 head of broccoli, cut into florets
- 1 head of cauliflower, cut into florets

- 1 onion, chopped
- 2 cloves of garlic, minced
- 1 inch ginger, peeled and grated.
- 1 tablespoon of turmeric powder
- 4 cups of low-sodium vegetable broth
- 2 cups of water
- Salt and pepper to taste
- Olive oil for cooking

Instructions:

1. Heat a large pot over medium heat, then add a tablespoon of olive oil. Once heated, add the onion and garlic, sauté until softened.
2. Add the grated ginger and turmeric powder to the pot, stir well, and cook for another minute.
3. Add the broccoli and cauliflower florets to the pot, stir to coat them with the onion, garlic, ginger, and turmeric mixture. Cook for 5 minutes or until the vegetables are slightly tender.
4. Pour in the vegetable broth and water, bring to a boil, then reduce heat to low and let simmer for 20-25 minutes or until the vegetables are fully cooked.
5. Using an immersion blender or transferring the soup to a blender, purée until smooth. If using a blender, be sure to work in batches and let the soup cool slightly before blending to avoid burns.
6. Return the pureed soup to the pot, add salt and pepper to taste, then reheat over medium heat until hot. Serve immediately with a drizzle of olive oil on top for added flavour.

7. This soup can be stored in an airtight container in the refrigerator for up to 5 days or frozen for up to 3 months. Reheat before serving.

This broccoli cauliflower soup with ginger and turmeric is not only delicious but also packed with nutrients that can help support overall health during pancreatic cancer treatment. The cruciferous vegetables provide fibre, vitamins C and K, while ginger and turmeric offer anti-inflammatory benefits that can help reduce inflammation in the body. This soup is also low in calories and carbohydrates, making it a great option for individuals following a pancreatic cancer diet that is low in sugar and fat. Enjoy!

Quinoa salad with roasted vegetables and feta cheese.

This quinoa salad is not only delicious but also packed with nutrients that are beneficial for individuals undergoing treatment for pancreatic cancer. Quinoa is a gluten-free grain that is high in protein and fibre, making it a great alternative to traditional grains. Roasting vegetables helps to bring out their natural sweetness and enhance their flavour, while feta cheese adds a tangy and salty taste. This salad is also low in fat and sugar, making it a healthy choice for those following a pancreatic cancer diet.

Ingredients:
- 1 cup quinoa, rinsed
- 2 cups vegetable broth
- 1 red bell pepper, sliced
- 1 yellow bell pepper, sliced
- 1 small red onion, sliced
- 1 small zucchini, sliced
- 2 tbsp olive oil
- Salt and pepper to taste
- 1/2 cup crumbled feta cheese
- 2 tbsp chopped fresh parsley
- Lemon wedges for serving

Instructions:
1. Preheat the oven to 400°F (200°C). Line a baking sheet with parchment paper.

2. In a large bowl, toss the bell peppers, red onion, and zucchini with olive oil, salt, and pepper. Spread them out on the prepared baking sheet and roast for 20-25 minutes or until tender and lightly browned. Set aside to cool.

3. In a medium saucepan, combine the quinoa and vegetable broth. Bring to a boil over medium-high heat. Reduce the heat to low, cover the pot, and simmer for 15-20 minutes or until the quinoa is tender and the liquid is absorbed. Fluff the quinoa with a fork and place it in a large mixing basin.

4. Add the roasted vegetables to the quinoa and toss gently to combine. Sprinkle the feta cheese

and parsley over the top of the salad and toss again. Serve immediately, with lemon slices to the side. Enjoy!

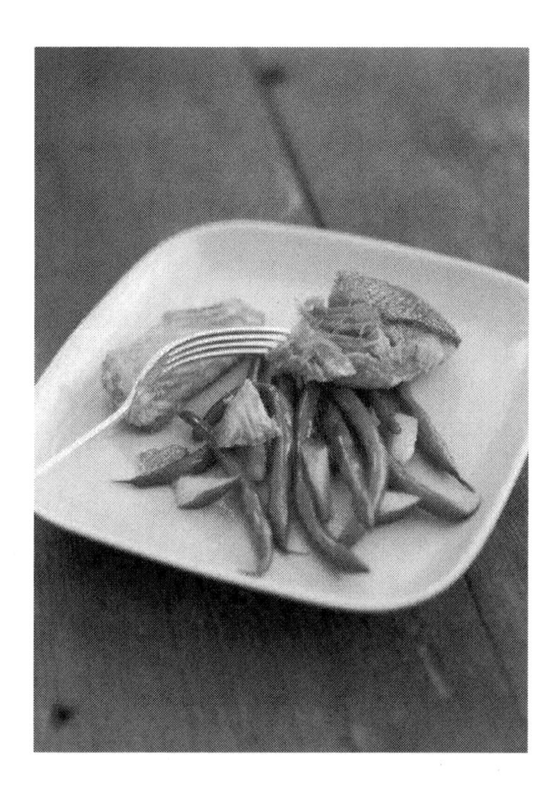

CHAPTER FOUR

Main Courses

Baked Salmon with Lemon and Herbs

Baked Salmon with Lemon and Herbs is a delicious and healthy main course option for individuals following a pancreatic cancer diet. This recipe is low in fat and sugar, making it a great choice for those with pancreatic cancer who may have difficulty digesting high-fat or sugary foods.

Ingredients:
- 4 (6-ounce) salmon fillets
- 2 lemons, thinly sliced
- 4 garlic cloves, minced
- 2 tablespoons chopped fresh parsley
- 2 tablespoons chopped fresh dill
- Salt and pepper, to taste

Instructions:
1. Preheat the oven to 375°F (190°C).
2. Arrange the salmon fillets in a baking dish, skin side down.
3. Layer the lemon slices over the top of each fillet.
4. In a small bowl, mix together the minced garlic, chopped parsley, chopped dill, salt, and pepper. Spread the mixture evenly over the top of each fillet.

5. Bake for 12-15 minutes, or until the salmon is thoroughly cooked and readily flaked with a fork.
6. Serve hot and enjoy!

This recipe is rich in omega-3 fatty acids, which can help reduce inflammation in the body and promote heart health. It's also a great source of protein and essential vitamins and minerals like vitamin D and potassium. For individuals with pancreatic cancer who may be experiencing digestive issues, this recipe is easy to prepare and digest due to its simple ingredients and minimal seasoning.

Grilled Chicken with Mixed Vegetables and Brown Rice

This healthy and delicious meal is perfect for individuals following a pancreatic cancer diet. It is rich in protein, fibre, and essential nutrients that can help support overall health and wellness during cancer treatment.

Ingredients:
- 4 boneless, skinless chicken breasts
- 1 red bell pepper, sliced
- 1 yellow bell pepper, sliced
- 1 zucchini, sliced
- 1 small red onion, sliced
- 2 tablespoons olive oil
- 1 tablespoon balsamic vinegar
- 1 teaspoon dried oregano
- Salt and pepper to taste

- 2 cups cooked brown rice

Instructions:

1. Preheat the grill to medium-high heat.
2. In a small bowl, combine the olive oil, balsamic vinegar, oregano, salt, and pepper. Set aside.
3. Brush chicken breasts with the olive oil mixture and grill for 6-8 minutes per side or until cooked through. Remove from the grill and allow to rest for a few minutes before slicing.
4. In a large skillet over medium heat, sauté the sliced bell peppers, zucchini, and red onion in the remaining olive oil mixture until vegetables are tender and lightly browned. Season with salt and pepper to taste.
5. Serve the grilled chicken with the mixed vegetables and brown rice on the side. Enjoy your healthy and delicious meal!

Tips:
- Brown rice is a great source of fibre and complex carbohydrates that can help keep you feeling full and satisfied. Rinse the rice before cooking to remove any excess starch and enhance texture. Cook according to package instructions using low sodium chicken broth instead of water for added flavour.
- Bell peppers are rich in vitamin C, which can help support the immune system during cancer treatment. Choose peppers that are brightly

coloured and firm to the touch. Remove seeds and membranes before slicing for easier digestion.
- Zucchini is a low calorie vegetable that is high in fibre and vitamins A and C. Slice into rounds or lengthwise strips for easy grilling or sautéing. Season with salt and pepper to taste before cooking for added flavour.

Lentil Shepherd's Pie with Carrots and Peas

Lentil Shepherd's Pie with Carrots and Peas is a delicious and nutritious main course that is perfect for those following a pancreatic cancer diet. This dish is packed with protein, fibre, and essential vitamins and minerals that are beneficial for individuals undergoing cancer treatment.

Ingredients:
- 1 cup rinsed and drained green lentils
- 4 cups vegetable broth
- 1 onion, chopped
- 2 cloves garlic, minced
- 2 carrots, peeled and chopped
- 1 cup frozen peas
- 2 tbsp olive oil
- Salt and pepper to taste
- 4 large potatoes, peeled and cubed
- 2 tbsp unsalted butter
- 1/4 cup milk
- Salt and pepper to taste

Instructions:

1. Preheat the oven to 375°F (190°C).
2. In a large pot, combine the lentils and vegetable broth. Bring to a boil, then reduce heat to low and simmer for 25-30 minutes or until the lentils are tender. Drain any excess liquid.
3. In a separate pan, heat the olive oil over medium heat. Add the onion, garlic, and carrots, and sauté for 5-7 minutes or until the vegetables are soft. Add the cooked lentils, frozen peas, salt, and pepper. Stir well to combine. Remove from heat and set aside.
4. In another pot, boil the potatoes until they are tender. Drain any excess water and mash the potatoes with butter and milk until smooth. Season with salt and pepper to taste.
5. Transfer the lentil mixture to a baking dish and spread it evenly. Spoon the mashed potatoes on top of the lentil mixture, spreading it out to cover the entire surface. Smooth out the top with a spatula or spoon.
6. Bake in the preheated oven for 25-30 minutes or until the top is golden brown and crispy. Let it cool for a few minutes before serving. Enjoy your Lentil Shepherd's Pie with Carrots and Peas!

This dish is rich in protein from the lentils, which are also a good source of fibre, iron, and folate. Carrots are an excellent source of vitamin A, while peas provide protein, fibre, and vitamin C. The mashed potatoes add some healthy carbohydrates to keep you energised throughout the day. This Lentil

Shepherd's Pie with Carrots and Peas is not only delicious but also nutritious and perfect for individuals undergoing cancer treatment who may have difficulty digesting meat or animal products due to chemotherapy or radiation therapy side effects.

CHAPTER FIVE

Sides and Snacks

Roasted Brussels Sprouts with Balsamic Glaze

Roasted Brussels Sprouts with Balsamic Glaze is a delicious and healthy side dish that is perfect for individuals following a pancreatic cancer diet. This recipe is easy to prepare and packed with nutrients that can help support overall health and wellbeing during cancer treatment.

Ingredients:
- 1 lb Brussels sprouts, trimmed and halved
- 2 tbsp olive oil
- Salt and pepper, to taste
- 1/4 cup balsamic vinegar
- 2 tbsp honey
- 1 tbsp Dijon mustard

Instructions:
1. Preheat the oven to 400°F (200°C). Line a baking sheet with parchment paper.
2. Rinse the Brussels sprouts under cold water and pat them dry with a clean towel or paper towels. Trim the ends and halve each sprout.
3. Spread the Brussels sprouts out in a single layer on the prepared baking sheet. Drizzle with olive oil

and season with salt and pepper, as desired. Toss to coat evenly.
4. Roast the Brussels sprouts in the preheated oven for 20-25 minutes, or until they are tender and lightly browned around the edges. Stir occasionally to ensure even cooking.
5. While the Brussels sprouts are roasting, prepare the balsamic glaze by combining the balsamic vinegar, honey, and Dijon mustard in a small saucepan over medium heat. Bring to a simmer and cook for 8-10 minutes, or until the mixture has thickened and reduced by half. Stir occasionally to prevent sticking.
6. Once the Brussels sprouts are done roasting, transfer them to a serving dish and drizzle with the balsamic glaze. Toss gently to coat evenly. Serve immediately as a side or snack.

This recipe is rich in fibre, vitamins C and K, and antioxidants, which can help support overall health and wellbeing during cancer treatment. The olive oil used in this recipe is also a healthy fat that can help support heart health, which is important for individuals undergoing cancer treatment as they may be at increased risk of cardiovascular complications due to chemotherapy or radiation therapy. Additionally, this recipe is low in sugar and salt, making it a healthy option for individuals following a restricted diet due to pancreatic cancer treatment side effects such as diabetes or high blood pressure. Enjoy!

Apple Slices with Peanut Butter and Cinnamon

Apple slices with peanut butter and cinnamon make a delicious and nutritious snack or side dish for individuals following a pancreatic cancer diet. This recipe is easy to prepare, packed with essential nutrients, and low in sugar, making it a healthy alternative to traditional snacks.

Ingredients:
- 1 medium-sized apple
- 2 tablespoons of natural peanut butter
- 1/4 teaspoon of ground cinnamon

Instructions:
1. Wash the apple thoroughly and remove the core.
2. Cut the apple into thin slices.
3. Spread a thin layer of peanut butter on each apple slice.
4. Sprinkle a pinch of cinnamon on top of the peanut butter.
5. Arrange the apple slices on a plate and serve immediately.

Nutritional Benefits:
This recipe is rich in fibre, healthy fats, and protein, which are essential for individuals undergoing pancreatic cancer treatment. Apples are an excellent source of fibre, which helps to promote digestion and prevent constipation, a common side effect of chemotherapy and radiation therapy.

Peanut butter is high in healthy fats and protein, which provide sustained energy and help to repair damaged cells in the body. Cinnamon has anti-inflammatory properties that can help to reduce inflammation in the body, which is often associated with pancreatic cancer.

Tips for Preparation:

- Choose ripe apples that are firm but not too hard or too soft. Apples that are too hard may be difficult to slice, while apples that are too soft may be mushy and difficult to spread peanut butter on.
- Use natural peanut butter that does not contain added sugars or artificial sweeteners. This will ensure that the snack is low in sugar and does not spike blood sugar levels, which can be beneficial for individuals with pancreatic cancer who may be at risk of developing diabetes as a result of their treatment.
- Use a sharp knife to slice the apples thinly to prevent them from browning too quickly. This will also make it easier to spread the peanut butter evenly on each slice.
- Store any leftover apple slices in an airtight container in the refrigerator for up to 24 hours. Reheat them in the microwave or oven before serving again to prevent any bacterial growth that may occur at room temperature.

Roasted sweet potato wedges with rosemary and sea salt.

Ingredients:

- 2 medium sweet potatoes, peeled and divided into wedges
- 2 tablespoons olive oil
- 1 tablespoon chopped fresh rosemary
- 1 teaspoon sea salt
- 1/2 teaspoon black pepper

Instructions:

1. Preheat the oven to 400°F (200°C). Line a baking sheet with parchment paper.

2. Rinse the sweet potatoes under cold water and pat them dry with a clean towel. Cut them into wedges, about 1 inch thick at the widest point.

3. In a large mixing bowl, combine the sweet potato wedges, olive oil, chopped rosemary, sea salt, and black pepper. Toss well to ensure that the wedges are evenly coated.

4. Arrange the sweet potato wedges in a single layer on the prepared baking sheet. Make sure they are not too crowded, as this will help them roast evenly.

5. Roast the sweet potato wedges in the preheated oven for 25-30 minutes, or until they are tender and

lightly browned on the outside. Flip them halfway through cooking to promote equal browning.

6. Remove the roasted sweet potato wedges from the oven and transfer them to a serving dish. Garnish with additional chopped rosemary, if desired. Serve hot as a side dish or snack that is low in fat and high in fiber, vitamins A and C, and potassium. Enjoy!

CHAPTER SIX

Desserts and Drinks

Berry Yogurt Parfait with Granola and Honey

Ingredients:

- 1 cup plain low-fat yoghourt
- 1/2 cup mixed berries (strawberries, blueberries, raspberries)
- 1/4 cup granola
- 1 tablespoon honey

Instructions:

1. In a small bowl, mix together the yoghurt and honey until well combined.
2. In a separate bowl, wash and dry the berries. Cut the strawberries into small pieces.
3. In a glass or parfait dish, layer the yoghurt mixture, granola, and berries in any order you prefer. Repeat until all ingredients have been used up.
4. Serve immediately and enjoy!

This dessert is a healthy and delicious option for those undergoing treatment for pancreatic cancer. It is low in fat and sugar, while still providing protein from the yoghurt and fibre from the granola and berries. The honey adds a touch of sweetness without being overly indulgent. This parfait can be made ahead of time and stored in the refrigerator for up to 2 days.

Berry Yogurt Parfait with Granola and Honey is also a great choice as a breakfast or snack option for those following a pancreatic cancer diet. It is packed with nutrients that can help support overall health and wellness during treatment.

Desserts and Drinks in Pancreatic Cancer Diet Cookbook for Beginners:

In addition to Berry Yogurt Parfait with Granola and Honey, this cookbook includes a variety of other desserts and drinks that are both delicious and nutritious for those undergoing treatment for pancreatic cancer. Some of the other options include:

- Apple Cinnamon Oatmeal: A warm and comforting breakfast option that is high in fibre and low in sugar.

- Mango Smoothie: A refreshing drink that is packed with vitamins and minerals from the mango, while still being low in fat and sugar.

- Chocolate Avocado Pudding: A decadent dessert that is made with healthy fats from avocado instead of heavy cream or butter. It is also high in fibre from the cocoa powder.

- Carrot Cake Energy Balls: A healthy twist on a classic dessert that is made with whole foods like oats, dates, carrots, and spices like cinnamon and nutmeg. They are also high in protein from the nuts and seeds used in the recipe.

- Ginger Lemon Tea: A soothing drink that is made with fresh ginger root and lemon juice, which can help alleviate nausea commonly experienced during pancreatic cancer treatment. It is also low in sugar and caffeine.

These recipes are designed to be easy to prepare, using simple ingredients that are readily available at most grocery stores. They are also adaptable to individual preferences, allowing for substitutions or modifications based on dietary restrictions or personal taste preferences. The cookbook includes detailed instructions, nutritional information, and tips for preparing each recipe to ensure maximum flavour and nutrition. Whether you are looking for a quick snack or a special treat, this cookbook has something for everyone!

Banana Ice Cream with Almond Butter and Chocolate Chips

Banana ice cream is a delicious and healthy dessert option for individuals following a pancreatic cancer diet. This recipe is not only easy to make but also packed with nutrients that can help support the body during cancer treatment. In this cookbook for beginners, we will be sharing a simple recipe for banana ice cream with almond butter and chocolate chips.

Ingredients:

- 4 ripe bananas, peeled and sliced
- 1/4 cup almond butter
- 1/4 cup dairy-free chocolate chips
- 1/4 cup unsweetened almond milk
- 1 tsp vanilla extract

Instructions:

1. Place the sliced bananas in a blender or food processor.
2. Add the almond butter, chocolate chips, almond milk, and vanilla extract.
3. Blend until smooth and creamy, scraping down the sides as needed.
4. Transfer the mixture to a freezer-safe container and freeze for at least 2 hours or until firm.
5. Scoop the banana ice cream into bowls and enjoy!

This recipe is low in fat and sugar, making it a great choice for individuals with pancreatic cancer who may have difficulty digesting high-fat or high-sugar foods. Almond butter is a good source of healthy fats and protein, while the chocolate chips provide a sweet treat without adding too much sugar.

Almond milk is a dairy-free alternative to traditional milk that is low in calories and fat.

In addition to this dessert recipe, we will also be sharing some delicious and healthy drink options that are suitable for individuals following a pancreatic cancer diet. These drinks are not only refreshing but also packed with nutrients that can help support the body during cancer treatment. Here's one of our favourite recipes:

Ginger Turmeric Lemonade:

Ingredients:
- 1/2 lemon, juiced
- 1 inch fresh ginger, peeled and grated
- 1 tsp turmeric powder
- 1 tbsp honey (optional)
- 1 cup water
- Ice cubes (optional)
- Optional garnishes include lemon slices and fresh mint leaves.

Instructions:
1. In a blender or food processor, combine the lemon juice, grated ginger, turmeric powder, honey (if using), and water. Blend until smooth.
2. Pour the mixture into a glass filled with ice cubes (if desired). Garnish with lemon slices and fresh mint leaves (optional). Serve immediately!

This drink is packed with anti-inflammatory and antioxidant properties thanks to the ginger and turmeric. Lemon is rich in vitamin C, which can help support the immune system during cancer treatment. Honey (if using) adds a touch of sweetness without adding too much sugar. This drink is also low in calories and fat, making it a great choice for individuals following a pancreatic cancer diet who may have difficulty digesting high-fat or high-calorie drinks.

Mint Tea with Lemon and Honey (Hot or Cold)

Mint tea with lemon and honey is a refreshing and soothing beverage that can be enjoyed both hot and cold. It's not only delicious but also has several health benefits that make it an excellent choice for individuals undergoing pancreatic cancer treatment. In this cookbook for beginners, we'll explore how to prepare mint tea with lemon and honey as both desserts and drinks that are easy to prepare and packed with nutrients that can help manage the side effects of chemotherapy and radiation therapy.

Hot Mint Tea with Lemon and Honey

Ingredients:
- 1 cup water
- 2-3 fresh mint leaves
- 1/2 lemon, juiced
- 1 tablespoon honey

Instructions:
1. Boil water in a small pot.
2. Add mint leaves to the boiling water and let it steep for 5 minutes.
3. Remove the kettle from the heat and drain the tea into a mug.
4. Squeeze lemon juice into the mug and stir in honey until dissolved.
5. Serve hot and enjoy!

Benefits:
- Mint contains antioxidants that can help reduce inflammation, which is common during cancer treatment.
- Lemon is rich in vitamin C, which can help boost the immune system and improve overall health.
- Honey has antibacterial properties that can help prevent infections, which is essential during cancer treatment when the immune system is weakened.

Cold Mint Tea with Lemon and Honey

Ingredients:
- 4 cups water
- 6-8 fresh mint leaves
- 1/2 lemon, juiced
- 2 tablespoons honey
- Ice cubes (optional)

Instructions:
1. Boil water in a large pot.

2. Add mint leaves to the boiling water and let it steep for 10 minutes.
3. Remove the pot from heat and strain the tea into a pitcher or large jug.
4. Squeeze lemon juice into the pitcher and stir in honey until dissolved.
5. Add ice cubes (optional) to chill the tea or serve over ice cubes immediately.
6. Pour into glasses and enjoy!

Benefits:

- ☐ Cold mint tea with lemon and honey is a refreshing alternative to sugary drinks that can help hydrate the body during cancer treatment, which can lead to dehydration due to increased urination caused by chemotherapy or radiation therapy.

- ☐ The cold temperature of the tea can also help soothe a sore throat, which is common during cancer treatment due to radiation therapy or chemotherapy-induced mouth sores (mucositis).

- ☐ The high water content in this drink can also help prevent constipation, which is common during cancer treatment due to opioid pain medication use or dehydration caused by vomiting or diarrhoea

CHAPTER SEVEN

Nutritional Information and Meal Planning Resources

Nutritional Information for Each Recipe

The Pancreatic Cancer Diet Cookbook for Beginners recognizes the importance of nutrition in managing pancreatic cancer and its side effects. Therefore, each recipe in the cookbook includes detailed nutritional information, making it easy for patients and their caregivers to make informed food choices.

The nutritional information provided includes calories, protein, carbohydrates, fat, fibre, and sugar. This information is crucial for patients undergoing chemotherapy or radiation therapy, as these treatments can cause changes in appetite, taste, and digestion. Patients may experience nausea, vomiting, or diarrhoea, making it challenging to consume enough calories and nutrients. By choosing recipes with the right balance of nutrients, patients can maintain a healthy weight and manage any side effects they may be experiencing.

In addition to providing nutritional information for each recipe, the cookbook also includes meal planning resources. These resources help patients and their caregivers create a weekly meal plan that meets their dietary needs while considering their treatment schedule and preferences. The meal planning resources include tips for meal planning, a weekly meal planner template, and a grocery list template. These resources make it easy for patients to stay organised and ensure they have all the ingredients they need for the week's meals.

The cookbook also includes a section on supplements and vitamins that may be beneficial for pancreatic cancer patients. This section provides information on supplements that can help manage side effects such as fatigue, nausea, and diarrhoea. It also includes information on vitamins that may be deficient in patients with pancreatic cancer due to the disease or its treatment. Patients should always consult with their healthcare provider before starting any new supplement or vitamin regimen.

Overall, the Pancreatic Cancer Diet Cookbook for Beginners provides comprehensive nutritional information and meal planning resources to support patients during their cancer journey. By making informed food choices and following a healthy meal plan, patients can manage their symptoms and improve their overall well-being.

Tips for Adjusting Your Diet Based on Your Needs (e.g., Low Fat, Low Sugar, High Protein)

Adjusting your diet can be challenging, especially when dealing with a health condition like pancreatic cancer. However, making dietary changes can help manage symptoms, improve overall health, and support treatment. Here are some tips for adjusting your diet based on your needs:

1. Low Fat Diet:

- Limit saturated and trans fats by avoiding fried foods, processed meats, and full-fat dairy products.

- Choose lean protein sources such as chicken, fish, and legumes.

- Incorporate healthy fats like avocado, nuts, and olive oil in moderation.

- Opt for low-fat or fat-free dairy products like skim milk, low-fat yoghurts, and cheese.

2. Low Sugar Diet:

- Reduce intake of added sugars by avoiding sugary drinks, candy, and baked goods.

- Choose whole fruits instead of fruit juices or dried fruits that are high in sugar.

- Use natural sweeteners such as honey or maple syrup in moderation.

- Read food labels carefully to find hidden sugars in packaged goods.

3. High Protein Diet:

- Include protein at every meal to support muscle health and wound healing.

- Choose lean proteins such as chicken, fish, tofu, and lentils.

- Pair protein with complex carbohydrates like brown rice or whole wheat bread to provide sustained energy.

- Snack on protein-rich foods like hard-boiled eggs or Greek yoghurt between meals to prevent muscle loss.

In addition to these dietary tips, it's essential to maintain a balanced diet that includes a variety of whole foods from all food groups. Consult with a registered dietitian or healthcare provider for personalised guidance based on your specific needs and preferences. Remember to always prioritise your health and wellbeing above all else.

CHAPTER EIGHT

Lifestyle and Nutrition Tips

Incorporating Exercise and Physical Activity

Incorporating exercise and physical activity is just as important as following a healthy diet when it comes to managing pancreatic cancer. While a nutritious diet can help support the body during treatment and recovery, regular exercise can also improve overall health and wellbeing. In this section of our Pancreatic Cancer Diet Cookbook for Beginners, we'll provide some tips and suggestions for incorporating exercise and physical activity into your daily routine.

- Consult with your healthcare team: Before starting any new exercise program, it's essential to consult with your healthcare team. They can provide guidance on what types of exercises are safe and appropriate for your individual situation.

- Start small: If you're new to exercise, it's best to start with small, manageable goals. This could mean going for a 10-minute walk around the block or doing some gentle yoga poses. Gradually increase the duration and intensity of your workouts as you gain confidence.

- Find an activity you enjoy: Exercise doesn't have to be a chore! Look for activities that you genuinely enjoy, whether that's dancing, swimming, or hiking in nature. This will make it easier to stick with your routine and reap the benefits of exercise over the long term.

- Incorporate strength training: In addition to cardiovascular exercise, it's also important to include strength training in your routine. This can help build muscle mass, which can be beneficial for overall health and may help prevent muscle loss that can occur during cancer treatment.

- Make it a habit: Try to incorporate exercise into your daily routine as much as possible. This could mean taking a brisk walk during your lunch break or doing some yoga stretches in the morning before starting your day. Making exercise a habit will help it become a natural part of your lifestyle.

- Get support: Consider joining a fitness class or finding a workout buddy to help keep you motivated and accountable. Having support from others can make it easier to stick with your routine and achieve your goals.

- Listen to your body: It's essential to listen to your body and not push yourself too hard too soon. If you experience any pain or discomfort during exercise, stop immediately and consult with your healthcare team if necessary.

Remember, the most important thing is to find an exercise routine that works for you and fits into your lifestyle. By incorporating regular exercise into your daily routine, you'll be supporting your overall health and wellbeing during this challenging time.

Hydration and its Role in Pancreatic Cancer Nutrition

Hydration is often overlooked in cancer nutrition, but it plays a crucial role in supporting overall health and managing symptoms during treatment. In particular, staying hydrated is especially important for individuals with pancreatic cancer, as the disease and its treatments can cause dehydration, which can lead to a range of complications.

Dehydration is a common side effect of chemotherapy and radiation therapy, as these treatments can cause nausea, vomiting, and diarrhoea, leading to fluid loss. Additionally, pancreatic cancer can affect the body's ability to produce digestive enzymes, making it difficult for the body to absorb nutrients and fluids from food and drinks.

To combat dehydration, it's essential to drink plenty of fluids throughout the day. Water is the best choice for hydration, as it's calorie-free and helps flush out toxins from the body. Other hydrating beverages include herbal tea, coconut water, and clear broths. It's recommended to aim for at least eight glasses of water or other hydrating beverages per day.

In addition to drinking enough fluids, it's also important to eat foods that are high in water content. These include fruits like watermelon, strawberries, and cantaloupe, as well as vegetables like cucumber, celery, and lettuce. Eating these foods can help provide additional hydration and promote overall fluid intake.

It's also important to avoid sugary drinks and caffeinated beverages, as these can actually contribute to dehydration. Sugary drinks can cause spikes in blood sugar levels, leading to dehydration due to increased urination. Caffeinated beverages like coffee and tea can also have a diuretic effect, causing the body to lose fluids more quickly than it replaces them.

In summary, staying hydrated is crucial for individuals with pancreatic cancer during treatment. By drinking plenty of fluids throughout the day and eating foods that are high in water content, you can help prevent dehydration and support overall health during this challenging time. Remember to avoid sugary drinks and caffeinated beverages as much as possible to further promote hydration.

PANCREATITIS DIET

FOODS TO EAT & AVOID

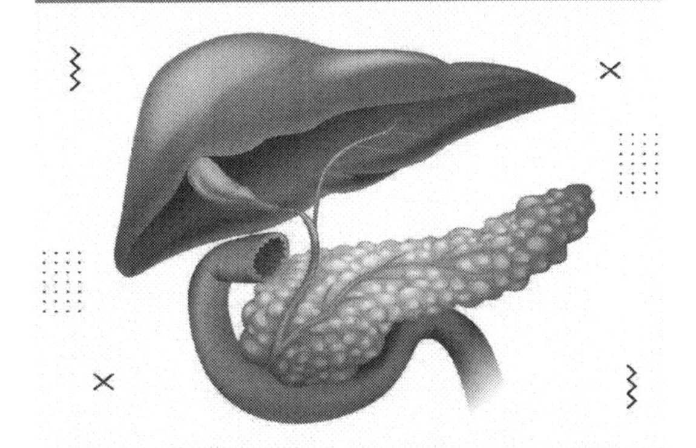

FOODS TO EAT	FOODS TO AVOID
Sweet potato	High-sugar foods
Coconut	Wafers
Barley	Beef and Pork
Coconut Water	Packaged Juices
Yogurt	Pizza
Blueberries	Pastries

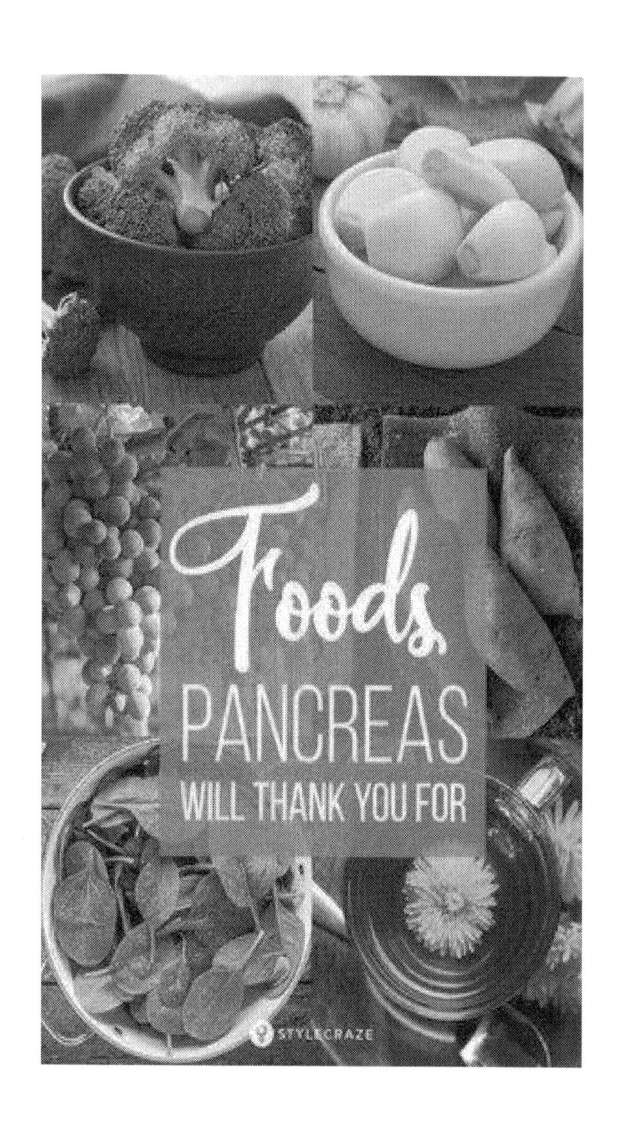
Foods
PANCREAS
WILL THANK YOU FOR
STYLECRAZE

CONCLUSION

Encouragement and Empowerment Through Nutrition

In conclusion, a pancreatic cancer diagnosis can be overwhelming and emotionally draining for both the patient and their loved ones. However, it is essential to remember that there are still steps that can be taken to promote encouragement and empowerment through nutrition during this challenging time.

Firstly, a nutritious diet can help to boost the patient's energy levels, improve their overall well-being, and potentially enhance their quality of life. By focusing on whole foods that are rich in nutrients, such as fruits, vegetables, whole grains, and lean proteins, the patient can nourish their body and provide it with the fuel it needs to fight against the disease.

Secondly, following a healthy diet can also provide a sense of control and empowerment during a time when so many other aspects of life may feel uncertain. By making conscious choices about what they eat, the patient can take an active role in their treatment plan and feel a sense of agency over their health.

Lastly, it is crucial to remember that nutrition is just one aspect of a holistic approach to pancreatic cancer care. Patients should also prioritize regular medical check-ups, emotional support from loved ones and healthcare professionals, and other complementary therapies as recommended by their healthcare team.

In this cookbook for beginners, we have provided a variety of recipes that are both delicious and nutritious, designed to make healthy eating easy and enjoyable. We hope that these recipes will inspire patients to embrace a healthy lifestyle and provide them with the encouragement and empowerment they need during this challenging time. Remember, small steps towards a healthier lifestyle can make a big difference in promoting overall well-being during pancreatic cancer treatment.

Made in the USA
Columbia, SC
10 November 2024